MYSTE

OF THE ANCIENT WORLD

THE
ALCHEMISTS

ROBERT JACKSON

WEIDENFELD & NICOLSON

LONDON

They were a strange and secretive brotherhood. They believed that they could obtain untold wealth by changing base metals such as lead and copper into silver and gold, and they embarked on a quest to discover a mysterious substance called the Elixir of Life, which they thought could prolong human existence.

*A*n illustration explaining *the alchemical process, from the 14th-century* **Treasury of Philosophy.**

le jeune ♂
ou ☿ ♃ celÿ
le ♃ qui
luy sert de
chaleur en
verrake
ennuiant

puis ou les
pieds sont
de l'humide
et en la bas
marquent
la sublimat
autre la ♀
ce qui y a
Tete et ♃ ra
les uns par
les ♃ ♃
ayi ÿ comp
tes pieds fa
pieles et la
teste avec
deÿ semble
et fÿ pare

Ѳ la po
te rouge
Sablier
composé
den 3 prÿ
♀ ☉ ♀ doÿ
estre tres
cettecÿ iu
le Sable
qui du que
y placé su
la tete de
Saturne p
Judicÿra ÿ
conducte ÿ
de l'opera
ou il est
retrograd
pao terp
detÿ a bel
du ☉ que
luÿ donne Si
force teli
y poudre ou
Estenceÿ
Laÿ ÿ mat
ou Essence
que Ѳ ceÿ

The Beginnings of Alchemy

They were the alchemists. They flourished throughout Europe in the Middle Ages, but the mystical science they practised – alchemy – is much older than that. It dates back at least 2,000 years to the days of ancient Greece. In fact, the word 'alchemy' comes originally from the Greek *chumeia*, which means the art of casting metals.

The early alchemists carried out many of their experiments in Alexandria, which in ancient times was a major centre of culture and learning. It was there

*T*he celebrated Pharos of Alexandria. Built in the reign of Ptolemy II, the lighthouse was one of the seven wonders of the ancient world.

*T*he Egyptian deity Thoth, wearing the symbols of creation on his head, stands before the God Ra. Thoth was identified with the Greek god Hermes Trismegistus, a symbolic figure in alchemy.

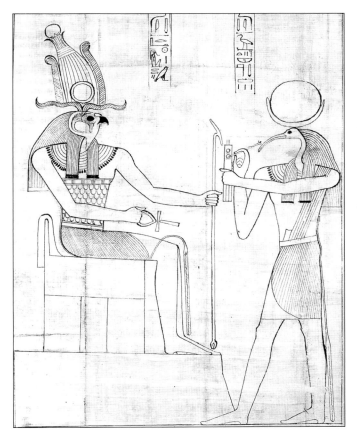

that the Greek *chumeia* became the Arabic *al-kimiya*, from which the modern 'alchemy' is derived. But alchemy was also practised in China and India in ancient times. The first written evidence of Chinese alchemy dates back to 144 BC, when the emperor issued a proclamation warning that anyone using alchemical gold to mint coins would be put to death. In India, there are references to alchemy dating from around the 2nd century BC, but since Alexander the Great's expedition to India took place in 325 BC, it is possible that the Indians learned the principles from the Greeks.

Alchemists believed that they could change base metals into precious ones – a process called transmutation – with the aid of something called the 'philosopher's stone'. The principles behind this theory were based on the ideas of the Greek philosopher Aristotle (384–322 BC), the tutor of Alexander the Great, who believed that everything in nature was subject to change. For example, seeds grow into grape vines, the grapes turn into wine, and wine turns into vinegar. So why, asked the alchemists, could lead and copper not be turned into silver and gold? All that was needed was a special substance to make it happen – the philosopher's stone.

The first alchemist we can identify by name is Bolos of Mendes, also known as Democritus, who lived in or near Alexandria in about 250 BC. He took his name from a Greek philosopher, Democritus of Abdera, who had died over 100 years earlier and who was the first person to form the theory that all matter was made of atoms.

Some of Democritus the alchemist's writings survive, and were discovered in Egypt in 1828. In them, he described various methods of making imitation gold. In one, the surface of another metal was coloured with a lacquer to make it look like gold, a process already well known in the world of ancient Greece.

An early 16th-century woodcut depicting alchemists at work.

Other early experiments were described in an encyclopedia of alchemy written by Zosimus around AD 300, parts of which have survived. Zosimus was a Greek historian, and his writings show that not all alchemists were men. A woman called Cleopatra was one (although she was not the famous Egyptian queen), and another was Maria the Jewess, a rather mysterious figure who invented several utensils which are still in use today. The *bain-marie*, a double pan for cooking sauces, is said to be named after her.

After the Roman conquest of Egypt the alchemists who had flourished in Alexandria and elsewhere were forced to go underground. The Romans were concerned that alchemical gold might be used to finance revolutionary factions, and when there was a rebellion in Egypt in AD 296 the Emperor Diocletian ordered the destruction of 290 manuscripts dealing with the manufacture of gold and silver by alchemical means.

The art of alchemy remained in the doldrums until AD 642, when the Arabs captured Alexandria from Byzantine rule. They soon became interested in alchemy themselves, and translated many works on the subject from Greek into Arabic.

An alchemist's water-bath, or bain-marie. The vessel is said to be named after its alleged inventor, Maria the Jewess, a noted alchemist.

A 17th-century copy of a treatise on alchemy originally written by the Arab alchemist Aidamir al Jildaki.

The most important Arab alchemist during this period was Jabir ibn Hayyan, who was court alchemist to Harun al-Rashid, the caliph of *The Arabian Nights*. As well as practising alchemy, Jabir ibn Hayyan invented processes for the manufacture of acids which remained in use for many centuries.

Alchemy in Medieval Europe

In the 11th and 12th centuries alchemy found its way into western Europe with the crusaders returning from their battles against the forces of Islam. The first translation of an

*T*he alchemist Albertus Magnus *reading from a manuscript grimoire, or magicians' textbook. He was also a noted astrologer.*

*N*orton's Ordinall. *Dating from the late 15th century, the book was used to initiate candidates into secret societies.*

alchemical book from Arabic into Latin was made in 1144 by Robert of Chester, and the translated works of Jabir ibn Hayyan were eagerly read by medieval philosopher-scientists.

Suddenly, a new scientific fervour gripped Europe. Was it really possible, as the ancients claimed, to acquire enormous wealth by means of transmutation? The quest was on, and it was to last for centuries.

Opinion in the scientific world of medieval Europe – a world very much in the grip of superstition, myth and wild speculation – was divided. One of the

ye may not w metalle or qwyk sylue begynn
To make Elixer if ye entende to wynn
yett if ye destroye there hole compilacion
Som of there cōpnentis wil help i 2dusio...
And that is nothing els of y con or that odu...
But only magncsia & litarge thr brodire...

itle page of **Alchimie de Flamel,**
a French manuscript purporting
to contain the secrets of the alchemist
Nicolas Flamel (1380–1418).

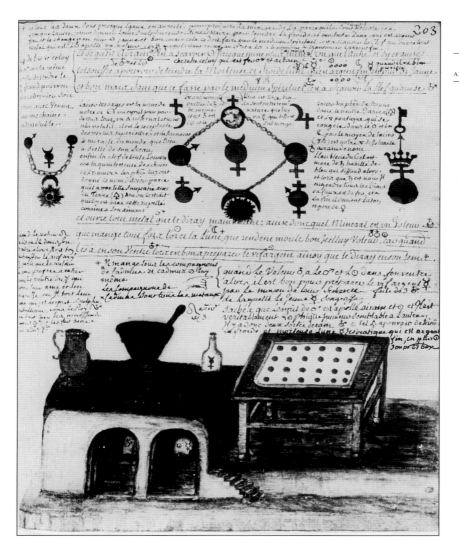

*A page from **Alchimie de Flamel** showing the arrangement of laboratory equipment and a planetary diagram.*

A German alchemist
in his laboratory,
aided by a sweating
servant. This picture is
attributed to Holbein.

leading thinkers of his time, Albertus Magnus (1193–1280) thought that it might be possible to create alchemical gold, but that it would be of inferior quality to pure gold. However, there was little open speculation about the techniques that might be used, simply because the practice of alchemy became a very secretive affair.

Many alchemists claimed to have achieved success, but not many were able to produce proof that their experiments had worked. One of the first was Nicholas Flamel (1330–1418), a notary at the University of Paris, who claimed to have dreamt about, and later found, a book containing the secrets of alchemy. With its aid, he succeeded in making the 'philosopher's stone', which he described as a red powder.

In 1392, he projected the powder on to half a pound of mercury, which was changed into the same quantity of silver. The experiment was witnessed only by his wife, but Flamel's contemporaries were inclined to believe his claim because of a sudden change in his circumstances. From having been a poor man he became quite wealthy, and donated money to several hospitals and churches in Paris.

Another man who believed that transmutation was possible was Jean-Baptiste van Helmont (1577–1644), a Flemish chemist and physician. Writing about the philosopher's stone, he said:

> I have divers seen it and handled it with my hands, but it was of colour such as saffron in its powder, yet weighty and shining like unto powdered glass. There was once given unto me one fourth part of one grain. I projected it upon eight ounces of quicksilver [mercury] made hot in a crucible, and straightway all the quicksilver with a certain degree of noise stood still from flowing and being congealed settled like into a yellow lump; but after pouring it out, the bellows blowing, there were found eight ounces and a little less than eleven grains of the purest gold.

Other scientists believed that mercury was the key to transmutation. One was

EFFIGIES PHILIPPI THEOPHRASTI
AB HOHENHEIM ÆTATIS SVÆ XLVII
OMNE DONVM PERFECTVM
A DEO

*P**ortrait of the Swiss alchemist Paracelcus (1493–1541).*

Sir Isaac Newton, known today as the 'father of modern physics', who spent many hours experimenting with it and suffered from mercury poisoning as a result. Newton's writings on alchemy amounted to some thousands upon thousands of pages, but they remain unpublished. (They were sold to private collectors in the 1930s.)

Some alchemists, however, believed that alchemy provided a foundation for serious scientific study. One was Philippus Paracelsus (1493–1541), a Swiss physician and alchemist who applied alchemical techniques to making medicines. He believed in transmutation, but his main concern was to prepare chemicals that would cure illness, rather than relying on traditional herbal remedies.

The Fraudulent Alchemists

Alchemy, naturally, was a fertile ground for fraud. One trickster was Simon Forman, who was born in 1552 and was imprisoned several times for false pretences. Having given up trying to make gold, he set about distilling love potions and strong drink, which was literally his downfall: his diaries record that he fell downstairs several times after a day's experimentation.

Some charlatans made a great deal of money through claiming to be able to manufacture gold. Domenico Caetano, an Italian who lived in the 17th century, persuaded the Elector of Bavaria to give him 60,000 florins – an enormous sum – so that he could set up an alchemical laboratory. When he failed to produce any gold, the Elector had him imprisoned, but he escaped after six years and turned up in Vienna, where he worked under an alias, the Count de Ruggiero. The Austrian Emperor Leopold employed him as the official court alchemist, and was considerate enough to die before Caetano was required to prove his claim.

The fraudster promptly offered his services to other European rulers, ending with King Frederick of Prussia. Like the others, Frederick parted with large sums of money, but he eventually saw through Caetano's confidence trick and had him hanged in 1709. Caetano was not the first alchemist to suffer the

This medallion belonged to the 17th-century alchemist Wenzel Seiler. The bottom part was supposedly transmuted into gold by Seiler on 16 September 1677; in fact the gold had been overlaid with silver, which dissolved when the medallion was dipped in nitric acid.

*T*he English
alchemist
John Dee (1527–1608).

*F*rontispiece to
A Little Book of
Love, *by John Dee.*

death penalty; Georg Honnauer was hanged in 1597 for failing to produce gold for the Prince of Württemberg, and Marie Ziegler was roasted alive for duping Duke Julius of Brunswick in 1575.

Queen Elizabeth I of England was not above being deceived; she employed an alchemist for two years before she sacked him. Another, John Dee, received a pension from Elizabeth on his return to England from Europe, where he had been operating with an accomplice, Edward Kelly. Their work was financed by Rudolf II, the Holy Roman Emperor, who eventually saw them for what they were and had Kelly thrown into prison. Dee would probably have suffered a similar fate had Rudolf not gone mad in the meantime. It is fortunate for us that he was spared, as he produced some of the foundation-stones of modern mathematics.

Yet another fraudulent alchemist, James Price – a member of the prestigious Royal Society because of his genuine

BELLUS ...... SACER

A *n alchemist's 'kitchen',*
or laboratory.

I *llustration depicting an alchemist*
minting gold coins.

scientific achievements – claimed to have converted mercury into gold and silver seven times in his laboratory at Guildford, in Essex, and published a paper about it in 1782. When the Royal Society put pressure on him to prove his claim, however, Price killed himself by drinking prussic acid – an admission of guilt if ever there was one.

One of the most delightful swindles concerned an Arabian alchemist, who set up business in Prague and invited the city's alchemists to witness a new process for multiplying gold. He would, he said, turn every 100 gold marks into 1,000. He duly invited 24 alchemists to his well-equipped laboratory, relieved them of 100 marks each and dropped the coins into a crucible. Then he placed

I llustrations from the 16th-century alchemical work **Splendor Solis,**
said to have originated in Augsburg, Bavaria.

Ora
Lege Lege Lege Relege labora
et Invenies.

another vessel, which he said contained various substances necessary for the experiment, inside a furnace.

A few minutes later, as the alchemists crowded round eagerly, the vessel exploded, filling the room with choking smoke. When it cleared, they found that the Arabian had vanished through a side window, along with their 2,400 gold marks.

The Mercury Connection

Throughout the history of alchemy, one thing stands out above all others: the alchemists' preoccupation with the heavy element, mercury. Quite apart from the fact that it resembled molten silver, serious alchemists believed that it possessed strange and mysterious powers.

Just how strange, modern science is slowly beginning to find out; but there is written evidence that ancient races knew far more about the extraordinary power of mercury than we of a modern age might think, and some of the most remarkable documentation comes from India.

Among the ancient Hindu sacred books we find the *Samarangana Sutradhara*, a collection of texts compiled in the 11th century but probably drawing on much older source material. The *Samarangana* contains 230 stanzas that describe in detail the building of aerial craft, called *vimanas*, in ancient Indian legend. Part of the text reads:

Strong and durable must the body be made, like a great flying bird, of light material. Inside it one must place the mercury-engine with its iron heating apparatus

A symbolic illustration from an alchemical work of 1702, showing the weighing and mixing of alchemical substances. The lower picture represents the conjunction of the sun and moon.

*F*ormula for the process whereby mercury, added to red sulphur, purifies and germinates the 'philosopher's stone'. From the 18th-century **Cabala Mineralis**, attributed to Rabbi Simeon ben Cantara.

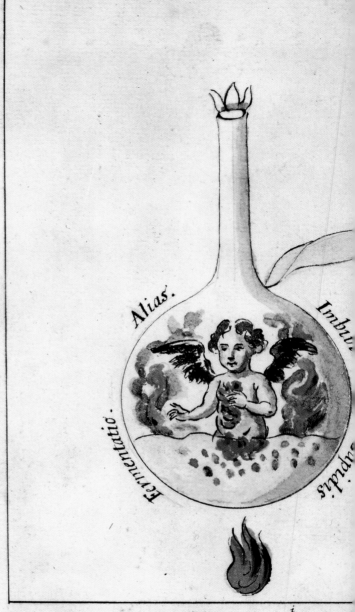

Alias.

Imbeu

Fermentatio·

updis

Sulfur Hoc Rvbeum Imbibitur noui ☿ Quinar
Pondere paulatim et Paulatim per septem
bibitiones et continuatio Calore Rotatā rot
vnoTranseunt Putrefactio et Iam Dicta Regim
mense Surgit Rex Omnipotens Seu Lapis noster p͂fect

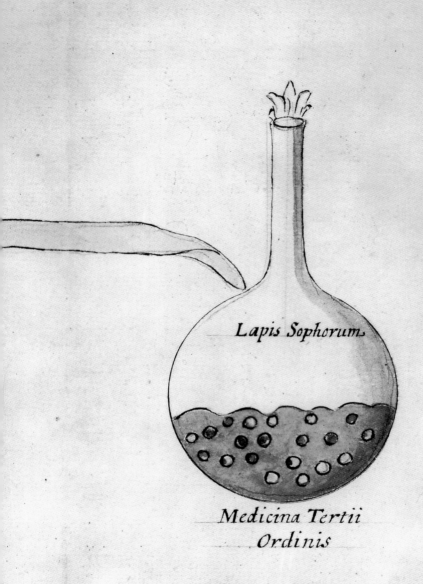

Lapis Sophorum

Medicina Tertii
Ordinis

<!-- Left margin column -->
i Corporis

sas Im=

uræ Men=
se

Finito.

ti nji
na 3 Ordi

Our Red Sulphur is Imbibed w:th 5 parts of new ☿ in Proportion t
the said Sulphur waight, and this by Seauen diuers Imbibitior
and w:th continuation of the heat. By the rotation of the wheele of
Nature, in a Months time is made Putrifaction & al the foresaid
Regimens, at the End of which month the King riseth Omnipoten
w:ch is our perfect Stone. The Medecine of the 3:th order capable
its projection to transmute al mettals = To God Eternal Prai

underneath. By means of the power latent in the mercury which sets the driving whirlwind in motion a man sitting inside may travel a great distance in the sky in a most marvellous manner . . . Similarly, by using the prescribed process, one can build a vimana *as large as the God-in-motion. Four strong mercury containers must be built into the interior structure. When these have been heated by fire from the iron containers, the* vimana *develops thunder-power through the mercury. And at once it becomes like a pearl in the sky.*

If the alchemists of the 17th and 18th centuries knew of such documents it might explain their fascination with mercury as a substance of great and hidden power; and such knowledge there certainly was, for their experiments

***A**llegorical illustration showing the transformation of mercury in the form of a snake nailed to a cross.*

***A** treatise on alchemy dealing with the preparation of alchemical materials and written in Indian script. It is dated August 1807.*

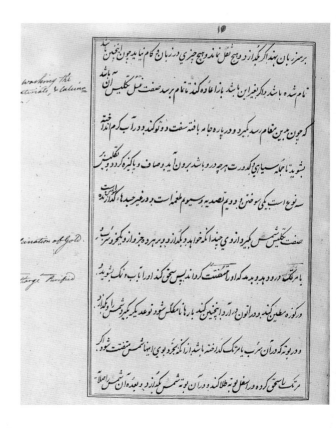

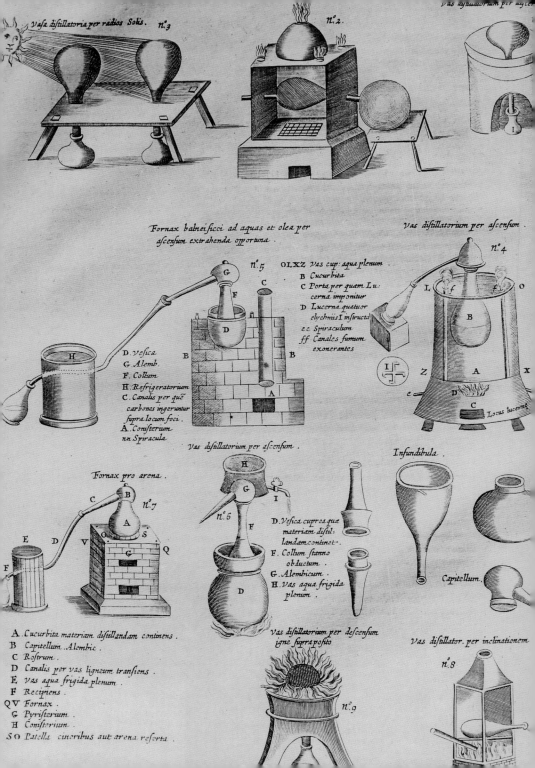

Vasa distillatoria per radios Solis.   n.º 3

n.º 2

Vas distillatorium per ascensum

Fornax balneisicci ad aquas et olea per
ascensum extrahenda opportuna.

n.º 5

Vas distillatorium per ascensum

n.º 4

O.L.X.Z Vas cup: aqua plenum.
B Cucurbita.
C Porta per quam Lu:
   cerna imponitur.
D Lucerna quatuor
   elychniis I instructa.
e.e Spiraculum.
ff Canales fumum
   exonerantes.

D. Vesica.
G. Alemb.
F. Collum.
H. Refrigeratorium.
C. Canalis per quē
   carbones ingeruntur
   supra locum foci.
A. Conisterium.
nn Spiracula.

Locus lucernæ.

Fornax pro arena.

n.º 7

Vas distillatorium per ascensum.

n.º 6

Infundibula.

D. Vesica cuprea quæ
   materiam distil:
   landam continet.
F. Collum stanno
   obductum.
G. Alembicum.
H. Vas aqua frigida
   plenum.

Capitellum.

A. Cucurbita materiam distillandam continens.
B Capitellum. Alembic.
C Rostrum.
D Canalis per vas ligneum transiens.
E Vas aqua frigida plenum.
F Recipiens.
QV Fornax.
G Pyristerium.
H Conisterium.
S O Patella cineribus aut arena referta.

Vas distillatorium per descensum
igne supra posito

n.º 9

Vas distillator. per inclinationem

n.º 8

*A*lchemical symbolism:
the 'Dove of the Spirit'
descends to form a trinity
with the 'Solar King' and
'Lunar Queen'. The imagery
represents the mystic
triangle.

A 1678 engraving
showing different
types of alchemical
ovens and detailing
their component parts.

unfolded at a time when India was yielding her cultural secrets to foreign explorers and merchants.

The British nuclear physicist Edward Neville da Costa Andrade (1887–1971), who collected many of Sir Isaac Newton's early scientific papers, noted in a speech delivered at Cambridge University in 1946 that Newton knew something about the secret of mercury. Quoting Lord Atterbury, a contemporary of Newton, Andrade said:

Modesty teaches is to speak of the ancients with respect, especially when we are not
familiar with their works. Newton, who knew them practically by heart, had the
greatest respect for them, and considered them to be men of genius and superior
intelligence who had carried their discoveries in every field much further than we

An engraving of 1702 showing the first distillation of alchemical products being offered to Luna, the moon god.

The solar king and lunar queen make love in the primeval waters. The sketch is symbolic of the dawn of creation.

today suspect, judging from what remains of their writings. More ancient writings have been lost than have been preserved, and perhaps our new discoveries are of less value than those that we have lost.

Quoting Newton, Andrade continued:

Because of the way by which mercury may be impregnated, it has been thought fit to be concealed by others that have known it, and therefore may be an inlet to something more noble, not to be communicated without immense danger to the world.

Immense danger to the world from mercury? What could that possibly mean?

The Modern Alchemists

In the early 1980s, rumours began to circulate that scientists had developed a strange and uniquely powerful explosive substance called 'red mercury'. At first its existence was considered to be a myth, but scientists today are taking it very seriously indeed. Not only is it something of immense power, it also has an application in nuclear-weapons' technology, and its existence could pose a serious threat to the world's attempts to stop the spread of nuclear weapons. Experts say that it could be used to make a baseball-sized neutron bomb.

This etching by Rembrandt shows an alchemist practising his art.

W As helffen *FACKELN*, *LICHT* und *BRILLEN*,
   Weil jedermann nach seinem Willen
In der *CHYMIA* ängstlich sucht,
Dasz ihm das *HERTZ* im Leibe pucht!
Er suchet zwar die creutz und qver,
Alleine *NICHTS* das findet er,
Und setzte er auf alle *Brillen*,
Weil er nur thut nach seinem Willen,
So vvird er doch nicht treffen an
Die *WAHRHEIT*, so erfreuen kan,
Versuchs, und lis das mit *VERSTAND*,
Und tapp nicht blindlings nach der *WAND*,
Gebrauch recht *FACKELN*, *LICHT* und *BRILLEN*,
So vvird *GOTT* deinen Wunsch erfüllen.

Scientists think that red mercury is a compound of mercury and antimony, bound together in a nuclear reactor. The alchemists of old attempted the binding of mercury and antimony, but they lacked the necessary technology.

Is it possible, then, that today's scientists have stumbled on a secret known to certain ancient races – that the element mercury, treated in a certain fashion, possesses extraordinary powers? And were the more serious alchemists, like Sir Isaac Newton, attempting to rediscover these powers? If so, then the declared aim of transmuting base metals into gold was a secondary one. But the irony is that the transmutation of elements is possible today – with the aid of nuclear physics. Without knowing it, the alchemists were experimenting with the dawn of the nuclear age.

*F**rontispiece of a 1708 German alchemical** work. The poem says 'What help are torches, light and glasses if you are not enlightened from within'.*

THE
ALCHEMISTS

PHOTOGRAPHIC ACKNOWLEDGEMENTS
Cover E.T. archive; pp. 2–3 Bridgeman Art Library
[BAL] / Bibliothèque Nationale, Paris;
pp. 4–5 AKG London; p. 5 Weidenfeld & Nicolson
Archives [W&N]; pp. 6–7 Fortean Picture Library
[FPL]; p. 8 BAL; p. 9 W&N; p. 10 FPL;
p. 11 BAL/British Library; pp.12, 13
W&N/Bibliothèque Nationale, Paris;
pp. 14–15, 17, 18 FPL; p. 20 W&N/Ashmolean
Museum, Oxford; pp. 20–21 BAL/Warburg
Institute, London; p. 22 ADK; p. 23 FPL;
pp. 24, 25 AKG; p. 26 W&N; pp. 28–9
W&N/British Library; p. 30 W&N/Bibliothèque
Nationale, Paris; p. 31 W&N/British Library;
pp. 32, 33 FPL; p. 34 W&N; pp. 35, 36–7, 38 FPL.

First published in Great Britain 1997
by George Weidenfeld and Nicolson Ltd
The Orion Publishing Group
5 Upper St Martin's Lane
London WC2H 9EA

A CIP catalogue record for this book is available
from the British Library
ISBN 0 297 823000

Picture Research: Suzanne Williams

Designed by Harry Green

Typeset in Baskerville